AILSAPRESS

Published by AILSAPRESS 2007
copyright © 2007   Ruth MacLean and Catherine Wilson
(this means no copycats allowed)

Printed by Summerhall Press Edinburgh

ISBN 978-0-9555656-0-1 paperback
ISBN 978-0-9555656-1-8 hardback

The Tail of Ailsa

RUTH MACLEAN
picture cut-outs

CATHERINE WILSON
verses

The book is dedicated to all mothers, our own
especially, and with gratitude to everyone who
has helped us on the way.

Ailsa is My Name

obody knows the home I'm from

Nobody knows its name

Whether you call me waif or stray

To me it's all the same . . .

I walked the streets in search of love

I'm so glad I came

I've found my Mum and she likes the sound

Of AILSA for my name!

My Best Bit

'm such a furry cat –

I've a dishy little nose

And I'm very proud of that!

Eyes of ice-green emerald

Set in velvet black

My whiskers are like arrows

Quivering on a bow

And my ears do point and harken

To things I do not know . . .

But though I love the bits in front

My best bit is behind

I leap I land I sit I sail

With my lovely bushy tail!

Mornings

he morning is my mellow time

I curl up in a ball

I pretend I'm here

I pretend I'm there

Where I am not at all.

Licking Me

hen my fur gets stickety

It likes to get a lickety

One paw in and one paw out

So I can turn my head about

And get my tongue into the bits

That are underneath my hips.

My Birthmark

have a secret birthmark

It's not for all to see

It's in a secret hiding place

Just for you and me!

Oh happy furry purry me,

Please stroke me on my tum,

Then just beneath that wispy curl

You can stroke my pretty pearl!

E g g s

 y goodness my gracious

I watched an egg go crack

It split in two and out of it

A yellow bit went splat!

DRINKING **S**ONG

My   fur   is   as   black   as   coal

Pr - pr pr - pr pr   pr   pr   pr   prrr

I   like   drinking from the   toi - let   bowl

Pr -pr pr -pr pr-pr-pr pr - pr pr   pr prrr!

The Sink

 love to watch the hole that drinks

Sitting there I think and think.

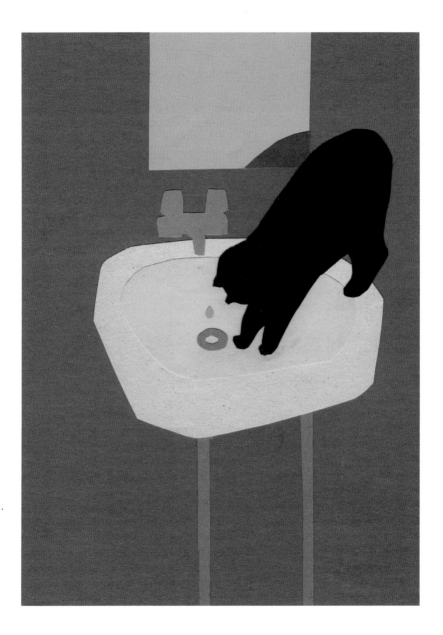

S h o w e r H o u r

ther cats cower

When they see the shower

As for ME —

I play here for hours!

Bedtime

very night at half past ten

My Mum climbs into bed

The bumps beneath the blanket show

Nothing but her head.

I crawl up close beneath her chin

Where it sticks out and her breath

breathes in . . .

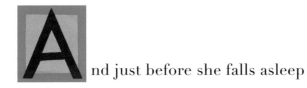nd just before she falls asleep

I lick her nose and bless her

cheek.

Alarm Call

Sometimes

I don't want to wait

You might sleep till half past eight

So then I clamber up on high

And make things tumble from the sky.

I scurry here   I scurry there

That should make you want to hurry

I even might switch on the light

To let you know it isn't night!

Nothing to Do

My Mum is knitting and I feel bad

I think I'll scratch beneath her bed

She doesn't like that it must be said

I think I'll chew a piece of wool

But though I'm bad I'm not a fool –

Oh dear oh dear, what will I do?

My Mum is knitting and I've

N o t h i n g   t o   D o.

On not being able to paint

I think I'll try to be a SAINT

I really will try NOT to paint

It's very hard for when I see

That lovely jar in front of me

And all those colours on the plate

And I know the brush can hardly wait ...

I think I'll only lift a paw

I promise you I'll do no more!

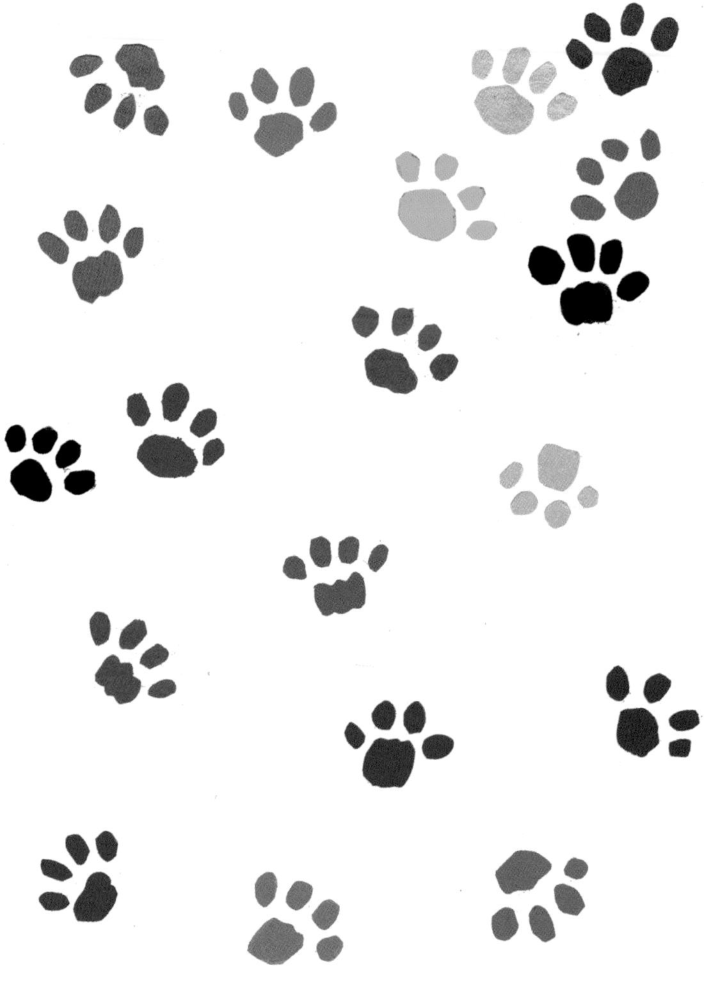

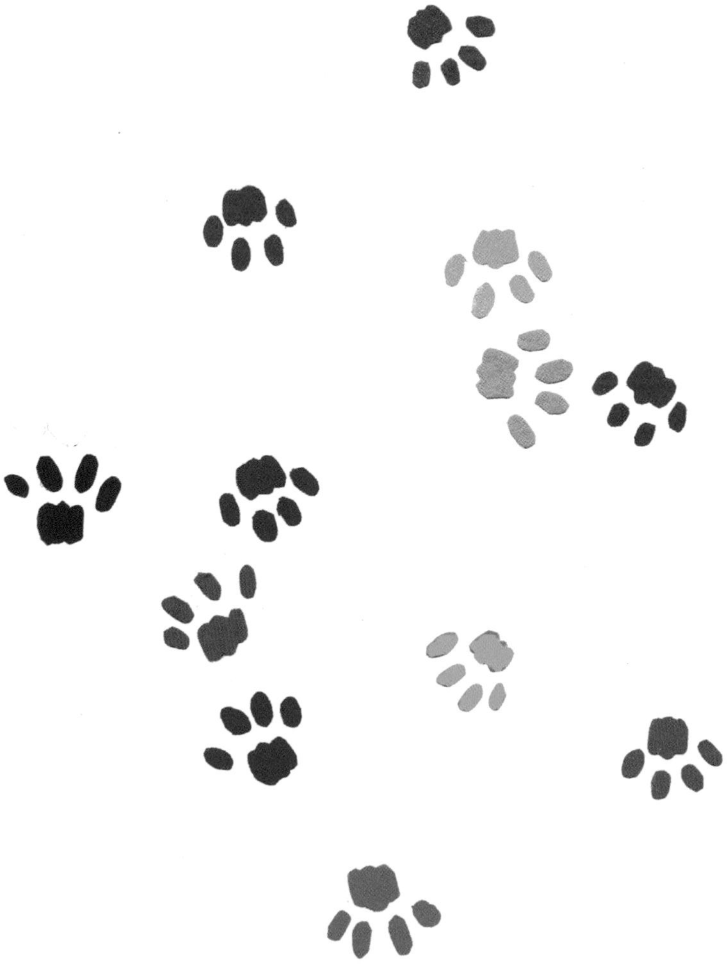

Y u m – Y u m

f I could only make one wish

I'd chews to be a tuna fish,

Yum – Yum!

i wonder

I wonder what will happen if

I spike my fur and wear a ring?

Will my Mum be in a miff?

Or will she think I'm just the thing?

Greeting

Purrr Purrr Prrurr

Is my friendly little greeting

When my Mum comes home

And I've been all alone

Prurr–Prurr–Prurr I like to say

Prurr–Prurr, had a nice day?

Spinning Wheel

ound and round

the merry–go–round

The spinning wheel does fly

My Mum is spinning out her yarn

And I'm helping the wheel to fly.

With each turn I stretch my paw

To catch between each spoke

The more I poke it spins the more

The more each spoke

Does stroke my paw.

Baking

hisks and tins and spoons and bowls

Sugar and spice and all things nice

Butter and eggs and flour and yeast

My Mum is baking us a feast!

Finishing Touch

ut of the oven, on to a plate

All of a sudden there is a cake!

She ices the cake to make it white

And just for good measure

           gives me a stripe.

Deedle-de-dee, deedle-de-dunk

She's baked a cake and I am a skunk!

Interlude

Life's a ball of wool lying on the ground

Rolled up in a ball just to be unwound

Life's for finding out

        whatever's to be found

And for taking the next leap

        whichever way it's bound.

W h i t e y

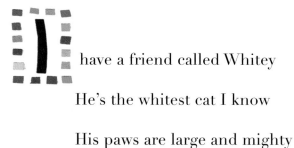 have a friend called Whitey

He's the whitest cat I know

His paws are large and mighty

His tail is straight and low.

I don't know where he comes from

It's a mystery to me

But in his rainbow kingdom

I'm as happy as can be.

Black and White

To see me in the pitch of night

You really have to shine a light

Though Whitey you can see from far

Because his coat's so awfully white!

But snowy coats no longer show

When there is a fall of snow

That's when Whitey disappears

And my black coat gets

three cheers!

Games with Whitey

hen Whitey climbs upon the pane

I ask him in to have a game

We chase our tails and hide and peek

I wish he'd stay at least a week!

Woolen Mouse

hen we're playing hide and peek

Whitey can be quite a sneak

He leaves me hiding in the house

And starts to chew . . .

              my woolen MOUSE !

Paws in Play

Ailsa:

See if I don't catch your paw

If you scratch me with your claw!

Whitey:

Why, this is such a tempting bait

Who can tell if I can wait?

Sometimes Whitey goes all still

He says he's bored, he's had his fill

So then I always wait a bit

And when he's least expecting it

I play my favourite game of all –

TICKLE AND POUNCE

Let's roll over in a ball!

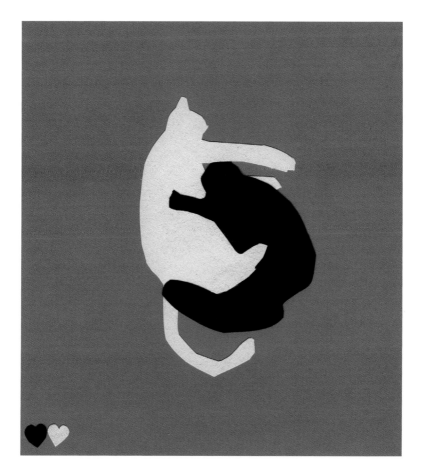

Food

My friend Whitey's awfully rude

He just comes in to get our food

I wonder that he feels no shame

To give us cats a dreadful name.

'm sorry Whitey please don't mind

I didn't mean to be unkind –

Please help yourself to ALL YOU CAN

I really am your ardent fan!

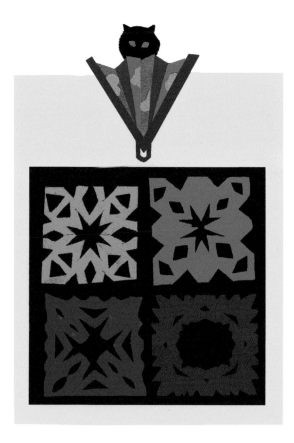

R i d d l e

hitey,

    here is a riddle

I'll give you a clue

There's one in the middle

Between me and you

One that is yellow

One that is blue . . .

If you give me the answer

I'll give you my paw

And say that I love you

For ever and more!

The answer is a JUG, you mug!

P i l l o w

esting on my pillow

In between the plants

I'm lying very still so

You will take a chance –

atch me if you can,

No before you even glance

I'll be off with you in tow

To lead another dance!

W h e r e   i s   h e?

on't want to stay in

Long to be playing

He's not to be seen

Is Whitey my friend

Or only a dream?

An Accident

here's a funny thing about my tail

It doesn't seem to want to sail

The end is cold and it is hanging

As if it got a dreadful banging!

ello, my dear Ailsa,

How do you do?

ot very well, sir

How do you?

OFF *with her* Tail!

I heard the vet say to my mother

I know my dear

        how much you love her

And if she could

        she'd grow another

As it is, I'm afraid to say

We cannot wait a single day –

I'm going to have to use

my KNIFE

For if I don't

she'll lose her life!

# POUT SONG

Prurr   Prurr   Prurr

Once I had a lovely tail

It was bushy and I could sail!

Prurr   Prurr   Prurr

Now I have a lovely spout

I'm unique without a doubt!

The Window Sill

itting on the window sill

Watching the passers by

Oh it's nice to be in

While others are out

I'll go out by and by.

Tub Call

Sthat Ailsa, how are you?

This is your friend from Katmandu.

Can you hear between the drips

A speaking voice that has no lips?

Oh dear oh dear, I've got to go,

Someone's tugging at my toe!

Birds

’m full of the joys of spring

tee–hee

A bird is singing upon a tree

I can't get him, he can't get me

I don't care a fig and neither does he!

P S

There are two birds upon the table

I would get them if I were able!

Screen Door

um, Mum, please come quick!

This really is a clever trick

I'm hanging here just like a bat

Who would think I am a cat?

L *e a p*

I leap with joy

I sing with glee

My friend Whitey

Comes to me!

Side by Side

ello Whitey,

where've you been?

Did you really see the Queen?

I have also lots to tell

I was sick and now I'm well.

Oh it's nice to have you here

I hope you stay at least a year!

If you wish I'll be your bride

And put our dishes side by side!

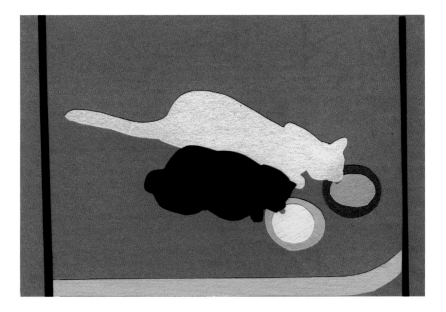

Tail Piece

f course we had kittens

And you can bet your mittens

They all had tails!

 The end.

AILSA took her final leap on February 14th 2007
after living a full and fascinating (*meow-wow!*) life.